LAST BARRIER TO FREEDOM
The Cyprus Detention Camps 1946 - 1949

Last Barrier to Freedom

The Cyprus Detention Camps 1946 - 1949

by Ruth Eis

Judah L. Magnes Museum
Berkeley, California
February 24 - May 19, 1985

" . . . for us who happen to have survived, these are sad reminiscences which chain us to the drastic reality of the catastrophic past. But those who were fortunate enough not to have experienced them and especially future generations should be aware . . . . But all of us should draw the only possible conclusion: NEVER AGAIN."

Vojtech Winterstein

Cover Illustration: Watch Tower and Tent, carved stone, Yosef Weissel

Photography: Sharon Deveaux

Catalog: Ruth Eis

Editor: Nelda Cassuto

Typography: Heyday Books

Printing: Albany Press

Table of Contents

Lenders of Objects to the Exhibition

Max Eis
Shemuel Katz
Morris Laub
The Music and Ethnology Museum,
   Haifa
Dov Noy
Shelomo Pappenheim
Hanoch Rinot
Yosef Weissel
Eli Wolf

Director's Foreword

The exhibition, "Last Barrier to Freedom—The Cyprus Detention Camps, 1946-49" reflects the historical research activities of the Magnes Museum and creative art detective work by Curator Ruth Eis.

When Morris Laub, the Joint Distribution Committee Director on Cyprus, presented his manuscript on the detention camps to the Museum for publication it became apparent that the experiences of the concentration camp survivors on Cyprus as well as the response of Jews and non-Jews to their plight represented a critical turning point in postwar Jewish history. Had the survivors become demoralized and lost their will for and vision of a life of freedom and security in the Jewish homeland and had the Jews of the world ignored them, the course of events would have been different, as would their impact on history.

Although Laub traces the development of the camps and depicts the political and social turmoil of their existence, he only hints at the richness of the creative expression which came out of them. Further indication of this richness was given by Miriam Novitch, curator of the Ghetto Fighters Museum, near Haifa, during her visit to the Magnes Museum. It remained, however, for Ruth Eis, during a mission to Israel to discover and select the materials now on exhibit here for the first time. By inspiring the artists and institutions to lend these materials, and by assembling them into an exhibit that enables us to experience the emotional intensity of the period, she has put us all in her debt.

The exhibit is the result of the creative participation of Magnes staff members Bill Chayes, Sara Glaser, Flo Helzel, Jeffrey Neidelman, Alice Perlman, Malka Weitman and Marni Welch. We thank Irma Silverman for her generous support. Morris Laub and Bezalel Amikam provided important guidance for research and organization.

We hope that this exhibition will help sustain our faith in the human spirit and our understanding of an entire post-Nazi generation's heroic efforts to create a haven for the persecuted.

Seymour Fromer
Director

Introduction

At the conference in San Remo, April 24, 1920, it was decided by the Supreme Council of the Principal Allied Powers that Great Britain should administer Palestine. Due to differences among some of the Powers, two more years passed before the Palestine Mandate was formally approved by the Council of the League of Nations on July 24, 1922, in London. During the time of the Mandate which lasted until 1948, Jewish immigration into Palestine was limited.

By 1939—mostly because Britain felt that the growth of a Jewish population and eventual statehood might become a threat to the empire—the infamous "White Paper" was issued which curtailed future Jewish immigration to 10,000 annually for five years, allowing in addition the entry of 25,000 refugees from Nazi persecution. So, precisely at the time when Hitler was planning the "Final Solution" for millions, hopes for reaching a "Jewish National Home" were dashed.

The persistent efforts of Palestinian Jews to rescue European survivors are by now part of history, as are the continuing policies of repression on the part of the British government. The interception and return of "illegal" refugee boats became a shameful page in the annals of diplomatic conduct.

During the latter part of the Mandate, so many boats filled with unhappy victims arrived that a detention camp was established at Athlit, on the coast about eight miles south of Haifa. Founded as a communal village by the Jewish Colonization Association (ICA) in 1903, this ancient Mediterranean seaport has a long history of occupation by people of many cultures. Canaanite, Roman and Crusader traces can be found near the agricultural station and the salt extracting plant which today are part of a new project where buildings are rising for yet another wave of immigrants. The old Crusader castle is visible from the modern highway, but the memory of the Athlit detention camp is kept alive in a museum. Adjacent to the Maritime Museum of the City of Haifa, it is aptly called the Museum of the Clandestine Immigration. There, in graphic description, we can follow the sequence of events: when Athlit was filled to capacity, new camps had to be opened and Cyprus was selected as the best suited location.

Between August 1946 and February 1948 approximately 52,260 persons passed through the Cyprus camps. The depth of the misery of their surroundings was equaled only by their disappointment in humanity: that this could happen after all they had experienced at the hand of Hitler's regime was inconceivable! For them the war had not ended—liberation was a sham.

Only one hope sustained these Jews: the hope of reaching the Promised Land. This hope permeated their actions, as illustrated most recently in the memoirs of Morris Laub, at the time administrator for the Joint Distribution Committee on Cyprus.

He describes how dedicated persons took measures to occupy the minds and strengthen the bodies of the inmates. Even an arts and crafts program took place under the leadership of such artists as Naphtali Bezem. This led us to investigate the possibility of finding art works created at the Cyprus camps. With this exhibition we bring a view from within, a look at the frustration as well as the inspiration among these people —and a hint of what might have been lost in human potential had it not been for the clandestine immigration.

Gathered for the first time are the personal expressions and memorabilia of a group of such variety as to defy description. They were held together only by their common misery. Now that they have been widely dispersed, their collective memory has been overshadowed by the important events of more than three decades in the land of Israel.

In the desire to preserve this segment of history before time can complete its obliteration, I went in search of evidence documenting activity in the arts.

The few objects I was able to retrieve were handcrafted by participants in a program established on Cyprus. Most pieces bear dedications to the teachers and helpers who came from Palestine to support the prisoners.

The major part of the exhibition consists of drawings, so striking in their impact that they compare to *Spiritual Resistance,* an exhibition of art from concentration camps, which toured North American museums during 1978-80. It had come from the collection of the Museum of the Ghetto Fighter's Kibbutz, located near Naharia, Israel. Art Curator Miriam Novitch had mentioned that among the 2000 works in the possession of the museum, a fair number came from the Cyprus detention camps. While I was making selections at the museum the idea to choose representative pieces by various distinctive artists took form.

Particularly through the examples of two artists, one the already established Abba Fenichel, the other a very young Shemuel Katz, we come to recognize and value the preciousness of human spirit.

After unspeakable suffering in the concentration camps of Europe and aboard obsolete boats, the tragedy of finding themselves in yet another hopeless situation could have broken their spirit, still they held on to faith and hope.

No charges were brought against these people; nevertheless, they were forcibly being detained at gunpoint. Undoubtedly it was the intense preoccupation with their stark surroundings, the exaggerated realism of tasks performed daily, which influenced these artists to such a degree that their style became literary, illustrative, and narrative in content. Again and again the pen or pencil returns to the thin line of barbed wire stretched into the horizon, to the watch tower as symbol of ever-present surveillance, and to the row of tents, giving what little shelter there was.

In view of the bleakness of such existence, it is remarkable to find so much humor in the drawings of Shemuel Katz. Perhaps it is an expression of gallows humor, the last resort of the human mind when all else seems to be failing. With the limited means at their disposal, the artists and artisans expressed their sensitivity to adverse conditions in strong terms. The pages of the portfolio on display remind one of the visual projection of emotions achieved by the German expressionists. Echoes of the graphic works by Kirchner or Heckel reverberate in the stark black and white renditions of laborers, in the predominance of diagonals and angular forms.

The emotional impact on the viewer is based on the very simplicity of these creations, on the straightforward personal dealing with the course of events not even understood. This incomprehension, this questioning, "Why are we doing this?" hovers under the surface in the treatment of such trite themes as a woman cleaning a tent or a man carrying water. Ultimately, we are confronted by the universal frustration of the captive soul, the cry for salvation "out of the depths I call upon the Lord."

Fortunately, the story does not end here—it continues in the lives of those who crossed this last barrier to freedom and arrived in Palestine.

During the decades that followed, these people went on to accomplish their respective goals in all fields of endeavor. They became a precious human resource. Had it not been for their unbreakable spirit of resistance and for the successful clandestine immigration, one dares not think of the loss.

To focus on the impact of their later achievements became a persistent idea while interviewing survivors and putting their tales on tape. Each story would have been an entity on its own, be that of the kibbutzniks of Gaaton and Neot Mordehai, the businessman in the city, the university professor, the leader in education, the nurse, the politician . . .

The leitmotif running through all the recollections was frustration and inability to comprehend: "What did we know? . . . I was just a kid . . . . After all the time I spent in German camps I thought the English were the liberators . . ." these were some of the comments. The irony of the last statement is overwhelming. A segment of history had bypassed these boys and girls while imprisoned. As if opening a time capsule, they had to learn the bitter lessons of power politics of the jittery British Empire, of economics and Arab unrest. Perhaps that is another story, a story kept alive in the sharply observant sketches of Shemuel Katz, who as artist-reporter became the chronicler of later important events.

We owe a debt of gratitude to the lenders of objects shown in the exhibition. In reassessing this period in their lives, the people I met were uniformly willing to share their thoughts and feelings. I deeply appreciate their help and their cooperation in giving of their time to this project. It is impossible to mention the names of all those who, in one way or another, contributed to the success of my mission; they share the rewards and satisfaction inherent in altruistic deeds.

Among those who gave assistance, I extend warm thanks to Miriam Novitch; to Trude Fraenkel, Hella Grossmann and Ruth Schindel for their valuable suggestions; I am indebted to the members of my family for their support; as the concept of this exhibition originated with the Magnes Museum so the execution is dependent on the teamwork and creative participation of the members of the museum staff, interns and volunteers: Bezalel Amikam and Morris Laub assisted in research; Florence Helzel and Jeffrey Neidelman prepared the catalog entries; Alice Perlman composed the captions; Marni Welch attended to the details of registration. The installation by Bill Chayes shows his flair for design at its best. Sara Glaser and Malka Weitman expertly handled publicity and related educational programs. The task of presenting an in-house created exhibition has been facilitated by the united effort of all departments; I am grateful to all who generously helped to make it a success.

R.E.

Exhibition Checklist

Works by Abba Fenichel
These works are on loan from the collection of Kibbutz Lohamei ha'Ghettaot

1
a) *La Faim*, 1947, Etching and drypoint, 10.5cm × 12cm.

b) *Enfant Juif*, ca. 1946, Pencil drawing, 10.7cm × 9.5cm.

2
Femme Cuisinant, 1947-48, Pen and ink, 12.8cm × 17.6cm.

3
Intérieur, 1947, Pastel, 23cm × 15.2cm.

4
Un Homme Lisant un Journal, 1947, Fusain, 14.6cm × 21cm.

5
Une Vielle Femme Lisant, 1948, Ink and brush, 24.5cm × 18.7cm.

6
Petite Fille á La Robe Rose, 1947, Pastel, 19cm × 27cm.

7
Deux Hommes dans une Baraque, 1947, Crayon, 21.5cm × 30cm.

8
Paysage Chypriote, 1946, Pastel, 32.5cm × 24cm.

9
Portrait d'une Femme, 1947-48, Pen and ink drawing, 17.2cm × 17.2cm.

10
Intérieur d'une Baraque, 1947, Pen and ink, 15.5cm × 23.5cm.

11
Femme dans une Baraque, 1947-48, Pastel, 17.6cm × 25cm.

12
Internés dans une Baraque, 1947, Pencil and crayon, 19.5cm × 20cm.

13
Vue de Murailles Au Chypre, 1946-47, Pen and ink, 9.3cm × 10cm.

14
L'Arrivée de Déportés, ca. 1947, Pen and ink, 8cm × 14cm.

15
Devant une Baraque, 1947, Pen and ink drawing, 18.5cm × 24.8cm.

16
Les Tentes, 1947, Fusain, 15cm × 10cm.

17
Vue du Camp, 1947, Charcoal, 18.5cm × 24.5cm.

18
Vue Générale, 1947, Pastel, 19cm × 28.2cm.

19
Vue Générale, 1947, Pastel, 19cm × 27.7cm.

20
Vue Générale, 1947, Pastel, 19.5cm × 27.7cm.

21
Un Coin du Camp, 1947, Charcoal, 12.5cm × 17.5cm.

22
Jeune Homme Assis, 1947, Blue ink drawing, 18.6cm × 11cm.

23
a) *La Foule*, 1948, Ink, 17.5cm × 25cm.

b) *Une Femme—Un Couple*, 1948, Ink, 17.5cm × 25cm.

24
Coin du Camp, 1946-48, Pastel, 19.3cm × 28cm.

25
Tête d'un Homme, 1947, Pastel, 27.2cm × 18cm.

26
Vue Générale, 1947, Pastel, 19cm × 28.5cm.

27
Un Coin du Camp avec L'Étoile de David, 1947, Ink and pencil, 16.3cm × 21cm.

28
Les Déportés, ca. 1946, Pen and ink, 9.5cm × 14cm.

29
Vue des Baraques avec un Couple, 1948, Pen and ink, 12.3cm × 17.5cm.

30
Les Tentes, 1947, Charcoal, 18cm × 24cm.

31
a) *Jeu de Dames*, 1948, Charcoal and paper, 22.7cm × 30.6cm.

b) *Le Lit*, 1948, Pen and ink drawing, 22.7cm × 30.6cm.

32
Vue du Camp avec Linge, 1947, Charcoal, 20.5cm × 23.5cm.

33
Works by Anonymous Artists
Cyprus 1947-49, Portfolio of 14 pages, Magnes Collection.

Works by Shemuel Katz
These works are on loan from the artist.

34
Illustration to Anderson Fairy Tales, 1983, Pen, ink and watercolor, 17.5cm × 14cm.

35
Keter Haggadah Page, 1971, Original layout of composite materials, 23.2cm × 20.2cm.

36
Kibbutz Artzi Haggadah Page, Ink and watercolor, 24.8cm × 12cm.

37
Sketch of Jan Peerce Giving a Concert for Refugees in Vienna, 1972, Pen and ink, 20.5cm × 28.4cm.

38
Sketch of Camp in Atlith, 1947, Watercolor, 18.5cm × 25.6cm.

39
Caricature of Airplane, 1948, Pen and ink, 24cm × 35cm.

40 (a and b)
Sketch of the First Day in Kibbutz Gaaton, 1948, Pen and ink, 16.8cm × 25.7cm.

41
Elath, 1949, Ink, 24.7cm × 34.4cm.

42
Caricature of Bedouins Drinking Espresso, Ink and crayon, 24.7cm × 34.7cm.

43
Fleeing Jenin, 1967, Pen and ink, 34.2cm × 48.4cm.

44
Kilometer 101 Checkpoint, 1973, Pen and ink, 25cm × 32.5cm.

45
Suez Canal, 1973, Pen and ink, 25cm × 32.7cm.

46
Synagogue in Alexandria, 1979, Pen and ink, 24.3cm × 34.3cm.

47
El Arish, 1979, Pen and ink, 22cm × 32.5cm.

48
Portrait of Sadat, 1979, Ink, signed by Sadat, 14.5cm × 25.7cm.

49
Dr. Burg with Torah Scroll, 1979, Ink on paper, 30.4cm × 22.9cm.

50
Hanukkah Celebration in Hotel Minah-House, Cairo, 1979, Pen and ink, 27cm × 22.2cm.

51
Abadan, Iran, n.d., Pen and ink, 25.1cm × 32.6cm.

52
Old Synagogue in Isphahan, 1975, Pen and ink, 35.1cm × 24.8cm.

53
Old Synagogue in Shiraz, 1975, Pen and ink, 33cm × 25cm.

54
Ghetto in Shiraz, 1975, Pen and ink, 33cm × 25cm.

55
New Synagogue in Isphahan, n.d., Pen, ink and crayon, 25.2cm × 33cm.

56
Mosque in Mashad, 1977, Pen and ink, 24cm × 34.2cm.

57
Holy Sepulchre in Mashad, 1977, Pen and ink, 34.6cm × 28cm.

58
Harbor of Khorramshar, 1975, Pen and ink, 32.6cm × 25cm.

59
Abadan, n.d., Ink, watercolor and crayon, 32.5cm × 50.2cm.

60
a)*Cyprus*, 1947, Pencil, 21cm × 26.6cm.
b)*Cyprus—Army Truck*, 1947, Pencil, 21cm × 26.6cm.

61
a)*Cyprus—Quonset Hut*, 1947, Sepia pencil, 17cm × 24.3cm.
b)*Cyprus—Exercise Yard*, 1947, Pencil, 20cm × 27.2cm.

62
Six Sketches from Lebanon, 1982, Pen and ink, 24.1cm × 33cm.

63
Ten Sketches of Transports to Cyprus, 1946, Pen and ink, 25cm × 35.5cm.

64
Album, 1946-47, 40 pages of original pencil, pen and ink drawings, watercolors and collages, the history of the artist's internment in camp, 20.3cm × 28.6cm.

Objects

65
Ketubah, Famagusta, Cyprus,
1947, Printed paper,
22cm × 35cm.

66
Textile Cover, Paint on tent
canvas, 1947, 29cm × 28cm.

67
The Cyprus Songster, Printed on
paper, 16.1cm × 21.5cm.

68
*"At The Threshold" Newspaper
from Cyprus Camp,*
Mimeographed on paper,
December 17, 1948,
31.5cm × 21.5cm.

69
Tent and Tower, Stone sculpture,
2.3cm × 3.8cm × 3.7cm and
6.1cm × 2.4cm × 2cm.

70
Commemorative Stone,
5.4cm × 9.9cm × 2.9cm.
Dedicated to Hanoch Rinot.

71
Commemorative Medal, 14K
Gold, 1949, 2.8cm diameter. "To
Mister Laub, friend of the
internees, in appreciation, the in-
ternees of Cyprus."

72
Commemorative Medal, 14K
Gold, 2.5cm diameter. "Tov
shem Tov"

73
Chess Set, Hinged box, wood
and stone. 3.4cm × 15cm ×
15cm.

74
Pin, made from a British silver
coin, 2cm diameter, "Cyprus,
Jewish Art Society"

75
Pin, Silver, 4cm × 3.5 cm. En-
graved with a picture of a ship.

76
New Years Card, Printed paper,
6cm × 9cm.

77
Handmade Jewelry Box, Wood
inlaid with stone, 1947, 22.6cm ×
15cm × 6.1cm.

78
Stone Plaque, 84.76.

79
*Notice of Protest Meeting at
Madison Square Garden, N.Y.,
Sponsored by the American
Zionist Emergency Council.*

80
Hanukkiah Stone, Carved lion
heads, dedicated to Dov Noy.

Artists' Biographies

Abba Fenichel

Born in Poland in 1906, a graduate of the Krakow Academy of Art, a qualified teacher of art since 1938. Prior to World War II, the painter participated in several exhibitions in Poland and some of his works were acquired by the Municipal Museum of Krakow.

A. Fenichel came to Israel after the War in 1948. He did illustration work for many books and published about 10 albums of graphic pages of illustrations. Among his subjects are portraits of the working man, immigration stories and actors' images. He is an art teacher at the Tel Aviv Museum. He has done hundreds of portraits of Israeli theater personalities, using a variety of techniques such as water color, pastel, ink, pen and brush. Most recently a number of his drawings and etchings are part of an exhibition in memory of Janusz Korczak in Hannover, Germany, the first time that works of Abba Fenichel are shown in that country.

Academic Studies
Academy of Art, Krakow, Poland

Collections
National Museum of Krakow, Poland
Bezalel Academy, Jerusalem
Artists' House, Ein Harod

M.A.
Painters' Assoc. of Kiev

One Man Shows
1938, 46 Artists' House, Krakow, Poland
1948, 1951 Micro Studio, Tel Aviv, Israel
1954 Katz Gallery Tel Aviv, Israel
1958 Shalom Asch Museum, Bat Yam
1960 Lochamei Ha'Ghettaot, Israel
1961 Artists' House, Jerusalem
1962 Eilat
1965 Rothschild House Yad Le'Banim Petach Tikva, Israel
1972 Dugith Gallery
1973 Dizengoff Gallery, Tel Aviv

Shemuel Alexander Katz

1926 - Born in Vienna

1938 - After the German occupation escapes with his family to Hungary. Studies first the piano to become a musician.

1944 - After Germany's occupation of Hungary is sent to concentration camp—later escapes to Budapest where he lives underground until the Red Army takes over.

1945 - Starts to study architecture. Joins *Hashomer Hatzair*.

1946 - Arrives illegally in Palestine and is immediately sent to Cyprus. There he holds his first exhibition. In 1947 he immigrates again and is one of the founders of Kibbutz Gaaton where he is still living with his wife and daughters.

1950-53 - Works as illustrator for *Mishmar Leyeladim*.

1953-54 - Advanced studies in Paris.

1955 - Illustrator and graphic designer for *Al Hamishmar*.

1958 - Travels in East Africa.

1962 - Studies in Paris, on scholarship of the French government.

1972 - Invited to join the permanent staff of Swiss weekly *Nebelspalter*.

1974 - Represents Israel at the memorial exhibition for *Nasr-e-din Hodja* in Istanbul.

1976 - Travels in Iran.

1979 - Twice visits Egypt with "autonomous" delegation. Granted a private interview with President Sadat.

1980 - Receives a six-month residential scholarship at the *Cité Internationale des Arts*, Paris.

1984 - Appearance of postage stamp "Flat to Rent" (Leah Goldberg) for his work with children's books.

Awards

1959 - Medal-International Exhibition "Art of the Book," Leipzig, Germany.

1960 - Prize-Annual Show of Humor, Bordighera, Italy.

196 - First prize for drawing and watercolour, Biennale of Young Artists, Paris.

1966 - Second Prize "Oscar for Humor," Bruxelles.

1969 - Medal-International Show of Humor, Italy.

1970 - Prize-Art of Humor, Expo, Montreal, Canada.

1974 - Prize "Nordau," Tel-Aviv.

Selected Bibliography and Readings Related to the Exhibition

Artists of Israel. 1920-1980 (Exhibition Catalog), The Jewish Museum, New York, 1981.

Bauer, Yehuda. *Bricha: Flight and Rescue.* New York: Random House, 1970.

Eliav, Arie. *Voyage of the Ulua.* New York: Funk & Wagnalls, 1969.

Laub, Morris. *The Last Barrier to Freedom.* Berkeley, Judah L. Magnes Museum, 1985.

Roth, Cecil. *A Bird's Eye View of Jewish History.* Union of American Hebrew Congregations, New York, 1954.

Seitz, Willliam C. *Art Israel.* 26 Painters and Sculptors, Museum of Modern Art, New York, 1964.

Ketubah, Famagusta, Cyprus, 1947

הסליט: נעמי דול
המנגינה: מאיר נוימן

ברכה לך, מולדת, מעבר לתייל,
חזון של דורות את, ארצי היעודה,
שובאינו לסווא יחסמו את הדרך;
בעוז נעגועינו תמס אף פלדה.
ברכה גם עליך, אחי הלוחם בה,
מעומק לבנו – חזק נא, חבר!
הנה, איך ניגר כאן הדמע מנחת,
הקסב, איך הולם כאן הלב המזמר:

מעמק הסבי, מאי קפריסין,
מארץ הדחי סלום לך, ארצי!
מאח ואחות, מזקן וילדון,
הסרים את סירך, סיר גבורה, נצחון.

כחץ מקסתות, כיונה מסוחררת,
יפליגו אליין סלומות של ברכה;
בכל התפוצות של גולה מתעוררת,
נסמע קול מצעד סל אלפי רבבה;
הזר לא יזכה לכבות הסלהבת –
אותה הצלו כיסופים ויאוס,
כי מרד הסער סל עם בן-אלמות
חזק מגדרות וחומות הגירוס.

מעמק הסבי, ...

סיידיס: דב

**Contemporary work by
Shemuel Katz. Dining Hall,
Kibbutz Gaaton.**